And God Said...

Written by Andrew Wilson

Illustrated by Rosie Dexter

10

British Library Cataloguing in Publication Data
A record for this book is available from the British Library

ISBN: 978-1-910587-95-9
Typeset by Diane Warnes
Printed in the UK

10Publishing, a division of 10ofthose.com
Unit C, Tomlinson Road, Leyland, PR25 2DY, England
Email: info@10ofthose.com
Website: www.10ofthose.com

The Story of Scripture

The story of the Bible could be told like this...

In the beginning, God.

Everything was shapeless,
and empty, and dark.

And God said, 'Lights.'
And it happened.

And God said,
and it happened.

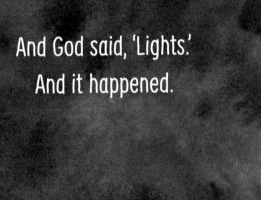

And God said,
and it happened.

And God said, and the earth did.

And God said, and the

animals did.

And God said, 'Go, have children, explore, rule,
guard, keep. Have the run of the place. Watch out for one thing
— that particular tree brings knowledge of good and evil, and you don't want
a piece of that — but otherwise, it's all yours. Enjoy.' And the humans did.

And the snake said, 'Did God really say that?
Are you going to let your lives be restricted by what you think he said?'

And the humans didn't. And it all went wrong.

And God said, and it happened.

And God said, and Abraham did.
And God said, and it happened.
And God said, and Israel didn't,
although sometimes they did,
but mostly they didn't.

And God said,
and it happened.

And God said,
'Here's my boy.
I love him.
Listen.'

And the snake said,
'Are you really the Son of God?
Why not do this, then?'
And Jesus said, 'It is written.'

And the snake said,
'Well, what about this, over here?'
And Jesus said, 'It is written.'

And the snake said, 'Or this?'
And Jesus said, 'It is written.'

And the humans said,

Who do you think you are?

WHAT ARE YOU PLAYING AT?

NOBODY CAN DO THAT EXCEPT GOD.

If you go there you'll be Killed.

Are you DEMONISED?

Are you MAD?

HE'S BLASPHEMING!

NO, MASTER, THIS WILL NEVER HAPPEN TO YOU.

And stuff like that.

And Jesus said,
'It is written in the scriptures.'

And the snake said,
'Give it up, Miracle Boy.'

And Jesus said,
'How else will the scriptures be fulfilled?'

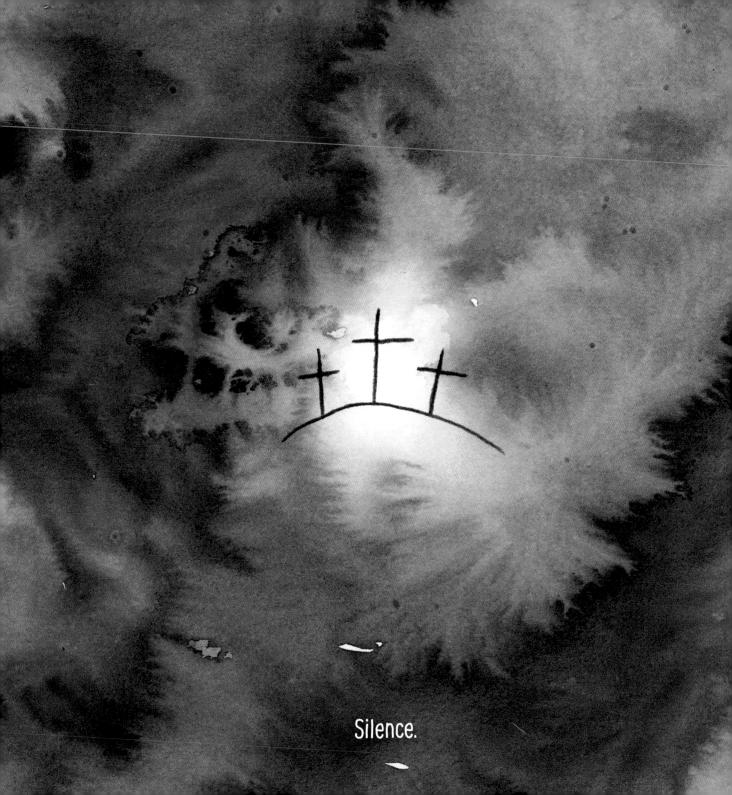

Silence.

And the humans waited.

And so did the angels.

And so did creation.

And so did the snake.

'Did God really say?' Silence.

And God said, 'Lights.'
And it happened.

That was the story of the Bible in outline.

God spoke... and made the world.

God spoke... and gave instruction to Abraham and the prophets.

God spoke... and performed great miracles.

God spoke... and brought forgiveness to those who did wrong to him.

God spoke... and Jesus rose from the dead.

Over and over again the Bible tells us that the devil tries to trick and deceive, and to get rid of God.

But God is greater than the devil, and God always wins.

When God promises... he comes through.

When God forgives... he forgives completely.

When God speaks... it happens.

10Publishing is the publishing house of **10ofThose**.
It is committed to producing quality Christian resources that are biblical and accessible.

www.10ofthose.com is our online retail arm selling thousands of quality books at discounted prices.

For information contact: **sales@10ofthose.com**
or check out our website: **www.10ofthose.com**